HANUKKAH AND CHRISTMAS AT MY HOUSE

Written and Illustrated by Susan Enid Gertz

Willow & Laurel Press

For my precious William and Laura.
May you always find joy in who you are.

For Tom, with whom life is a lovely adventure.

HANUKKAH AND CHRISTMAS AT MY HOUSE

Copyright 1991 by Susan Enid Gertz
First Printing January 1992

Published by Willow & Laurel Press, Box 51,
Middletown, OH, 45042.
Printed and bound in the United States of America.

Library of Congress Catalog Card Number: 91-73702
International Standard Book Number
0-9630934-0-1

A note to adult readers—

I am delighted that you have chosen to read *Hanukkah and Christmas at My House* to the son, daughter, grandchild, or young friend in your life.

I wrote this story to give my young children the opportunity to see their interfaith family's way of life positively represented in a book that is geared to their age and interests.

I chose to write about Hanukkah and Christmas because, although these two holidays have different religious meanings, their seasonal proximity and spirit of celebration connect children and adults alike.

The book's message—for the interfaith child, and all children—is that families of all religions love their children and their traditions, and the joy of the holidays comes from that love.

Interfaith families can find additional support and information in *Raising Your Jewish/Christian Child* (Newmarket Press) by Lee F. Gruzen.

S. E. Gertz

*W*hen my mommy was a little girl, she waited all year for Hanukkah. She told her mama and daddy, "I love everything about Hanukkah!"

When my daddy was a little boy, he waited all year for Christmas. He told his mama and daddy, "I love everything about Christmas!"

*W*hen cold weather came and it was Hanukkah-time, my mommy would sit on her daddy's lap while he told her the Hanukkah story. He told her about how brave Judah Maccabee rescued the Temple from the Syrians.

He also told her about the special oil lamp in the Temple. It had only enough oil to stay lit for one day. My mommy loved to hear how the lamp surprised everyone by burning brightly for eight days and nights.

At Christmas-time, my daddy would sit on the big soft couch while his daddy told him the Christmas story. His daddy told him about Mary and Joseph riding a donkey to Bethlehem one night. And he told him about all the animals in the barn where Mary and Joseph slept.

My daddy loved to hear about baby Jesus being born that night. He thought, "Mary and Joseph loved that baby, just like my mama and daddy love me!"

My mommy always helped her mama fry crispy potato latkes for Hanukkah supper. Mommy loved to hear the sizzle as her mama plopped spoonfuls of potato into the oil. They fried yummy doughnuts too, and mommy sprinkled them with cinnamon and sugar.

My mommy could never wait until after supper to eat a crispy, sweet doughnut. She always ate just one when her mama wasn't looking!

$\mathcal{M}$y daddy helped his mama roll out spicy gingerbread dough for Christmas cookies. He liked to pick out the cookie cutters and press them into the dough. After they had cut out lots of snowmen, Santas, angels, and stars, his mama put the cookies into the oven.

My daddy could hardly wait to eat one! When the cookies were done, he picked out the biggest to eat. His mama always said, "Wait until it's cool." But my daddy could never wait!

When my mommy was a little girl, she loved to light the menorah and sing the Hebrew blessings. Her mama and daddy lit the "helper" candle that lights all the others. Then she carefully touched the helper candle to each candle in the menorah.

The last night was the best. My mommy loved to see her family around the table with their faces shining in the bright light of all eight candles.

When my daddy was a little boy, he loved to decorate the Christmas tree while Christmas songs played on the radio. His whole family liked to sing along. My daddy's favorite song was "Deck the Halls." His mama and daddy would lift him high enough to put the beautiful angel on the tree. He carefully put her lacy skirt over the tallest branch.

Turning on the tree's colored lights was the best part. My daddy loved to see his family all around with their faces shining in the light of the Christmas tree.

*E*ach night of Hanukkah, after lighting the menorah and eating supper, mommy and her family sang Hanukkah songs, played dreidle games and opened gifts. My mommy's favorite song was "I Had a Little Dreidle."

One year, my mommy saw her name on a big package on the floor. She rushed to open it. Inside was a doll house her daddy had built for her! It had real furniture and a little family to live inside. My mommy hugged and kissed her mama and daddy.

"I love you!" she said.
"I love everything about Hanukkah!"

On Christmas morning, my daddy would wake up early to see what Santa had brought. There were always presents from his mama and daddy, too. Everyone would take turns opening presents.

One year, my daddy saw his name on a big package under the tree. He rushed to open it. Inside was the shiny red tricycle he had seen at the toy store! It had brightly colored streamers on each handle. My daddy hugged and kissed his mama and daddy.

"I love you!" he said.
"I love everything about Christmas!"

Now my mommy and daddy are grown up and I'm their little girl. My brother and I wait all year for Hanukkah and Christmas. We always tell them, "We love everything about Hanukkah *and* Christmas!"

On Hanukkah, we tell the story of the Maccabees and the Temple lamp. We fry latkes and doughnuts, sing the blessings, and light the menorah. We sing Hanukkah songs and open gifts.

On Christmas, we tell the story of Mary, Joseph, and baby Jesus. We bake cookies, decorate the tree, sing Christmas songs, and open presents.

We all love having Hanukkah and Christmas. In my family, we wouldn't want it any other way!

NO-PEEL POTATO LATKES *(Makes 10–12 3″ pancakes)*

Ingredients

1 egg	1 tablespoon oil
1 small onion, quartered	1/4 teaspoon sugar
3 cups unpeeled, cubed potatoes	1/2 teaspoon salt
3 tablespoons flour	1/8 teaspoon pepper
	oil for frying

Place the egg and onion in the blender and blend for a few seconds. Add half the potatoes. Blend until smooth. Add rest of potatoes and remaining ingredients (except oil for frying). Blend until smooth. Drop by spoonfuls into a well oiled frying pan. Fry on each side until brown and crispy. Drain on paper towel. Serve with apple sauce or sour cream.

ORANGE JUICE DOUGHNUTS *(Makes about 30.)*

Ingredients

3/4 cup orange juice	2 eggs, beaten
1/2 cup margarine	dash of salt
4 tablespoons sugar	oil for frying
2 pkg. dry yeast	cinnamon
3–4 cups flour	powdered sugar

Combine orange juice, margarine, and sugar in a saucepan. Heat until margarine melts. Pour in a mixing bowl, cool to lukewarm, and add yeast. Stir until dissolved. Add eggs, salt, and three cups flour and mix. Knead until smooth. If dough is sticky, add more flour as needed. Place dough in a greased bowl and cover. Let rise in a warm spot for half an hour. Shape small pieces into rings, balls, or braids. Cover and let rise another half hour. Deep fry in hot oil. Drain and let cool slightly. Put a few teaspoons of powdered sugar and cinnamon in a paper bag. Add doughnuts and shake.

Don't Forget—*Cooking with hot oil can be very dangerous. Make sure that a grown-up is helping you.*

My Daddy's Favorite Christmas Recipe

Chewy Gingerbread Cookie
(Makes about 30 thick and bready, not-too-sweet cookies.)

Ingredients

3/4 cup melted butter or margarine
1 cup molasses
1/2 cup honey
1 cup buttermilk
6 cups all-purpose flour

1/2 teaspoon salt
2 teaspoons ginger
4 teaspoons baking powder
3/4 teaspoon baking soda
1 tablespoon orange or
    lemon extract

Preheat oven to 350.

In a large mixing bowl, mix the melted butter or margarine, molasses, and honey until smooth. Add the buttermilk and lemon or orange extract. Mix the flour with the salt, ginger, baking powder, and soda. Add flour mixture to molasses mixture. Mix to a smooth, stiff dough. Roll out on a lightly floured surface to about 1/3 inch thick. Cut into shapes. Place on ungreased baking sheet.

Bake for 10 to 12 minutes. Cool on racks. Decorate with favorite frosting or icing and small bits of candy or fruit.

Don't Forget—*Cooking with a hot oven can be very dangerous. Make sure that a grown-up is helping you.*

HISTORICAL SETTING OF HANUKKAH

Hanukkah, the Feast of Lights or the Feast of Dedication, commemorates the Maccabees' recapturing of the Temple in Jerusalem from the Syrians and its rededication in 165 BCE (Before the Common Era). The events commemorated in the celebration of Hanukkah occurred about 1,000 years after the time of Moses and the exodus from Egypt and about 100 years before Rome conquered Jerusalem.

At the time of the Maccabean revolt against Syria, the country we now call Israel was divided into a northern kingdom (Israel) and a southern kingdom (Judea). Judea was occupied by a Syrian king named Antiochus IV. When Antiochus IV became king, he inherited an empire on the verge of bankruptcy, internally unstable, and with powerful enemies on all sides. Antiochus decided that his empire would be more stable if everyone had Greek religion and culture in common and decreed that all inhabitants of Judea were to worship Greek gods. At this time, Antiochus didn't care if Jews continued practicing their own religion along with the worship of Zeus.

Judean contact with Greek culture had begun long before Antiochus IV. Such contact reached back to the Persian, Greek, and then Egyptian occupation of Judea from the years 539–198 BCE. When Antiochus made his decree, many Jews already spoke Greek, read Greek translations of the Torah (first five books of the Hebrew bible), and had adopted many aspects of Greek culture. Although the influence of Greek culture was strong, controversial rival parties—radical pro-Hellenic, moderate pro-Hellenic, and fundamentalist conservative—had emerged in previous years and were still a powerful influence on Jewish life in Antiochus' time.

Although many pro-Hellenic Jews did not resist Antiochus' decree, a strong conservative element would not allow Zeus-worship at the Temple in Jerusalem.

When stronger laws had no effect on this minority resistance, Antiochus plundered the Temple, killing 40,000 Jews in the process. Nevertheless, the conservatives continued the resistance to Hellenization. In 167 BCE, during another attempt to force compliance, Antiochus completely outlawed the practice of Judaism in Judea. The worship of Zeus was forcibly established in the Temple, all copies of the Torah were destroyed, circumcision of baby boys was prohibited, observance of the Sabbath and the festivals was forbidden, and Jews were forced to eat food they considered unclean. The punishment for defiance was death.

Not long after Judaism was outlawed, officers of the King were sent around the country to enforce the decree. Rather than comply, a local priest named Mattathias took his five sons and fled to the hills. Mattathias and his five sons launched a guerrilla-style war against both the Syrians and the Jews who accepted the Hellenization of Jewish culture. They eventually turned their minority resistance into a full-fledged revolt. The third son Judas, who took over leadership after his father's death, was nicknamed Maccabeus. Some sources say this nickname means "the hammer." The army became known as the Maccabees.

In 165 BCE, the Maccabees finally reclaimed and then rededicated the Temple in Jerusalem by purifying it, burning incense, and relighting the branched lamps called menorahs that stood in the courtyard. A few years later, the Maccabees drove Antiochus out of Egypt and established self-rule for the first time since 539 BCE. Maccabean rule didn't last long however. The power of Rome was growing, and by the first century Common Era (CE) Judea was part of the Roman empire. By 70 CE the Temple in Jerusalem was permanently destroyed.

HISTORICAL SETTING OF JESUS' BIRTH

Historians agree that Jesus carried on his ministry in the third decade of the Common Era, during the reign of Tiberius and the procuratorship of Pontius Pilate. However, the year and place of his birth are uncertain. Mark and John say nothing about them; Matthew 1 and 2 and Luke 2 present widely divergent accounts of Jesus' birth and childhood. In Matthew 1 and 2, Jesus' birth is set at the time of Herod I and the change of regime, which would be about 4 BCE. In Luke 2, Jesus' birth is linked to the first registration in Judea under the Emperor Augustus, which was about 6 CE.

The tradition of naming Bethlehem as the place of Jesus' birth is found in Matthew 2 and Luke 2. In Matthew, Bethlehem is thought of as the parents' original place of residence, which they soon change to Nazareth because of dangers threatening their child. In the Lucan story, Jesus' parents really live in Nazareth, but stay in Bethlehem temporarily because they are obliged to register at the Davidic family's place of origin.

Jesus' lifetime was a period of international stability under the rule of the Romans. However, in Judea considerable unrest and division existed among several rival groups. Three of these—the Sadducees, Pharisees, and Essenes—had begun to emerge during the period of Maccabean rule that preceded the Romans. The Sadducees were a religiously conservative, but politically adaptable, group who accepted the written Torah alone as authoritative. The Pharisees were more liberal, for although they stressed the performance of all of the commandments of the Torah, they also accepted a revealed oral tradition and reinterpreted the Torah and prophetic writings to meet the needs of the times. They did not feel strongly about politics as long as they could practice Judaism undisturbed. The Essenes were distinguished by their pursuit of a ascetic, monastic life and their disdain for material goods.

The Zealots emerged afterwards, during the rule of the Romans. They were a radical group who refused to pay taxes and were intent upon fomenting revolution against the Romans. They were particularly dedicated to keeping the Temple pure.

Within the context of these diverse streams of tradition, Jesus went about teaching a message with many themes in common with both the Pharisees and Essenes, and yet in important respects distinct.

CLOSING THOUGHTS

The Pharisaic movement gained strength over the years of Roman occupation and ultimately gave rise to modern Rabbinic Judaism; the life and teachings of Jesus gave rise to modern Christianity. One of the most fascinating challenges facing Jews and Christians today, particularly those in interfaith households, is clarifying the relationship between these two religious communities. We may ask ourselves, "What values, beliefs, and visions do these two traditions share? At what points do they differ? How can they be best applied in our work for peace and justice in the world?"